The Royal Horticultural Society
Diary 2004
Botanical Drawings

JOHN LINDLEY (1799 – 1865)

Commentary by Brent Elliott

TED SMART

Frances Lincoln Limited
4 Torriano Mews
Torriano Avenue
London NW5 2RZ

www.franceslincoln.com

The Royal Horticultural Society Diary 2004: Botanical Drawings

Website: www.rhs.org.uk

Astronomical information reproduced, with permission, from data supplied by HM Nautical Almanac Office, copyright © council for the Central Laboratory of the Research Councils.

British Library cataloguing-in-publication data
A catalogue record for this book is available from the British Library

ISBN 0-7112-2222-3

Printed in Italy

First Frances Lincoln edition 1998
This edition produced for The Book People Limited, Hall Wood Avenue, Haydock, St Helens WA11 9UL

RHS FLOWER SHOWS 2004

All shows feature a wide range of floral exhibits staged by the nursery trade, with associated competitions reflecting seasonal changes and horticultural sundries. With the exception of the shows held at Torquay, Malvern, Chelsea, Wisley, Hampton Court and Tatton Park, all RHS Flower Shows will be held in one or both of the Society's Horticultural Halls in Greycoat Street and Vincent Square, Westminster, London SW1.

The dates given are correct at the time of going to press, but before travelling to a Show, we strongly advise you to check with the Diary Dates section of the RHS Journal *The Garden*, or telephone the 24-hour Flower Show Information Line (020 7649 1885) for the latest details.

EUROPEAN NATIONAL HOLIDAYS 2004

AUSTRIA	Jan. 1, 6; April 11, 12; May 1, 20, 30, 31; June 10; Aug. 15; Oct. 26; Nov. 1; Dec. 8, 25, 26
BELGIUM	Jan. 1; April 11, 12; May 1, 20, 30, 31; July 21; Aug. 15; Nov. 1, 2, 11; Dec. 25
DENMARK	Jan. 1; April 8, 9, 11, 12; May 7, 20, 30, 31; June 5; Dec. 25, 26
FINLAND	Jan. 1, 6; April 9, 11, 12; May 1, 20, 30; June 26; Nov. 6; Dec. 6, 25, 26
FRANCE	Jan. 1; April 11, 12; May 1, 8, 20, 30, 31; July 14; Aug. 15; Nov. 1, 11; Dec. 25
GERMANY	Jan. 1, 6; April 9, 11, 12; May 1, 20, 30, 31; June 10; Aug. 15; Oct. 3, 31; Nov. 1, 17; Dec. 25, 26
GREECE	Jan. 1, 6; Feb. 23; March 25; April 9, 11, 12; May 1, 30, 31; Aug. 15; Oct. 28; Dec. 25, 26
ITALY	Jan. 1, 6; April 11, 12, 25; May 1; Aug. 15; Nov. 1; Dec. 8, 25, 26
LUXEMBOURG	Jan. 1; Feb. 23; April 11, 12; May 1, 20, 30, 31; June 23; Aug. 15; Nov. 1, 2; Dec. 25, 26
NETHERLANDS	Jan. 1; April 9, 11, 12, 30; May 5, 20, 30, 31; Dec. 25, 26
NORWAY	Jan. 1; April 8, 9, 11, 12; May 1, 17, 20, 30, 31; Dec. 25, 26
PORTUGAL	Jan. 1; Feb. 24; April 9, 11, 25; May 1; June 10; Aug. 15; Oct. 5; Nov. 1; Dec. 1, 8, 25
SPAIN	Jan. 1, 6; March 19; April 8, 9, 11, 12; May 1, 30; July 25; Aug. 15; Oct. 12; Nov. 1; Dec. 6, 8, 25, 26
SWEDEN	Jan. 1, 6; April 9, 11, 12; May 1, 20, 30, 31; June 26; Nov. 6; Dec. 25, 26
SWITZERLAND	Jan. 1; April 9, 11, 12; May 1, 20, 30, 31; Aug. 1; Nov. 1; Dec. 25, 26

JOHN LINDLEY

1799–1865

John Lindley was born on 5 February 1799. His father was George Lindley, a nurseryman at Catton, near Norwich, whose book *The Orchard and Kitchen Garden* John later edited for publication. In 1818 he went to London and, through his friend William Hooker, found employment helping with the arrangement of Robert Brown's herbarium in Sir Joseph Banks's library. After Banks's death in 1820, Lindley was hired by William Cattley of Barnet to publish the *Collectanea botanica*, a series of illustrations of plants from Cattley's collection.

In 1821, Lindley began working for the Horticultural Society as an artist, his specific brief being to draw roses. He excelled, and in the following year was appointed Assistant Secretary at the Society's new garden at Chiswick, his duties being 'to have superintendence over the collection of plants, and all other matters in the Garden'. It was at Chiswick that Lindley established shows with competitive classes, to which the origins of the modern flower show can be traced. It was also during this period that he wrote his first paper to be published in the Society's *Transactions*: 'A sketch of the principal tropical fruits which are likely to be worth cultivating in England for the dessert' (volume V, 1821–1822). In 1827 he was elevated to the position of Assistant Secretary to the Society as a whole, with duties at both Chiswick and its London offices. As Assistant Secretary he also acted as the editor of the Society's publications – first the *Transactions*, and then the *Journal*. In 1841 he was appointed Vice-Secretary to the Society.

One of his specialities was the identification of plants sent back by the Society's collectors. From the 1820s to the 1840s, the Society sent emissaries to every continent to discover new plants of potential garden interest. Among them were John Damper Parks, who introduced yellow roses from China; Theodor Hartweg, who brought back the ancestors of the modern fuchsia from Mexico; Robert Fortune, who made his first expedition to China for the Society; and best known of all, David Douglas, after whom the Douglas fir was named. Lindley's work on the plants these explorers sent back resulted in a wide range of new plant names being coined. Some of the plants are illustrated in the following pages.

His work for the Society did not prevent Lindley from accepting a range of duties elsewhere. At the age of twenty-nine he was elected Professor of Botany at the newly founded University of London, a post he held for over thirty years. From 1835 to 1853 he was also Professor of Botany to the Society of

Apothecaries, a role which brought with it the responsibility of being director of the Chelsea Physic Garden.

Lindley's name as an horticultural editor grew through work outside the Society. From late in 1827 until 1830, he edited the *Pomological Magazine*, a fruit journal modelled in format on Curtis's *Botanical Magazine*. In 1815, Sydenham Edwards, a former artist for Curtis, had started a rival magazine called the *Botanical Register*, and Lindley became its editor in 1829. One of the earliest published accounts of Australian plants, Lindley's important 'Sketch of the vegetation of the Swan River [an Australian colony]' appeared in this magazine in 1839. Then, together with Joseph Paxton, he founded the *Gardeners' Chronicle* in 1841 and *Paxton's Flower Garden* (three volumes, 1850–1853). The former became the longest-running horticultural periodical, and Lindley remained editor until his death.

Lindley's spectacular energy and enthusiasm involved him in further extra-curricular activities. In 1838 he compiled a report on the condition of the royal gardens at Kew, which led to the establishment of the Royal Botanic Gardens, of which his old friend William Hooker was made the first Director. He was also active on the 1845 commission to enquire into the causes of the Irish potato blight; a juror for food products at the Great Exhibition of 1851; and for many years he was consulted by the Admiralty about the planting of the island of Ascension.

Lindley's great passion for the family of the Orchidaceae began with his work for William Cattley, after whom he named the genus *Cattleya*. He was the first botanist to work out a classification of orchids, and wrote prolifically on the subject, his most notable works being the *Sertum orchidaceum* (1838–1841) and *The Genera and Species of Orchidaceous Plants* (1830–1840). He coined the names of approximately eighty orchid genera still recognised today, including *Cattleya, Coelogyne, Laelia, Lycaste* and *Miltonia*. He has been called the father of modern orchidology, and the American Orchid Society named its scientific journal *Lindleyana* in his honour.

Among his numerous other works were: *Rosarum monographia* (1820); *Digitalium monographia* (1821); *Synopsis of the British Flora* (1829); *Introduction to the Natural System of Botany* (1830); *Fossil Flora of Great Britain* with William Hutton (1831–1837), long the standard work in English; *Ladies' Botany* (1834); *Key to Structural and Systematic Botany* (1835); the text for the last volumes of Sibthorp's *Flora Graeca* (1835–1837); *Victoria Regia* (1837); *Flora Medica* (1838); *Theory of Horticulture* (1840); *Elements of Botany* (1841); *The Vegetable Kingdom* (1846); and the initial botanical text for E. J. Ravenscroft's *Pinetum Britannicum* (1863).

In 1858 Lindley was finally promoted to Secretary of the Society. He held the office during the period when its name was changed to the Royal Horticultural

Society. Failing health brought his contribution to public life to an end after he helped organize the Great Exhibition of 1862. This sequel to the exhibition of 1851 was held in the RHS's new gardens in Kensington. On his retirement a public subscription was raised for him, and E.V. Eddis painted his portrait, which now hangs in the library named after him. After an incredibly full life, his last years were spent suffering from a failing memory and 'softening of the brain'; he died on 31 October 1865.

Lindley left an unintended double legacy to the world. He married in 1823 and had three children, and for several years the Lindley family lived at Bedford House, Acton, near the Society's garden. After his death, this estate became the site of London's first garden suburb, Bedford Park, the course of whose streets was planned in order to preserve as many of Lindley's trees as possible.

His second legacy was the Lindley Library. In 1859 the Horticultural Society sold its library during a period of financial retrenchment. When it could afford to begin to replace this loss, using profits from the International Botanical Congress and Horticultural Exhibition, the Society purchased Lindley's personal library to serve as the nucleus of a new collection. In 1868, the library was invested in the Lindley Library Trust (which is now administered by the RHS as sole Trustee) in order to ensure that it could never be sold again. Lindley's acquisitions now form the cornerstone of the world's greatest horticultural library.

Of the plants named after Lindley the following are still available : *Aeonium lindleyi*, *Buddleja lindleyana*, *Corydalis lindleyana*, *Photinia lindleyana*, *Rhododendron lindleyi* and *Salix lindleyana*. There are other plants currently available that were once named after Lindley, but which are now known by other names: *Bignonia lindleyana* (now *Clytostoma callistegioides*) and *Sorbaria lindleyana* (now *S. tomentosa*).

Brent Elliott
The Royal Horticultural Society

Front cover

Tacsonia (now *Passiflora*) *manicata*, a hand-retouched chromolithograph by Louis-Aristide-Léon Constans (*fl.* 1830s–1860s), from the first volume of *Paxton's Flower Garden* (1850–1851) by John Lindley and Joseph Paxton

Title page

The 'Cannon Hall Muscat' grape, a hand-coloured engraving after a drawing by Augusta Innes Withers (1792–1869), from the *Transactions of the Horticultural Society* (1832), in which the fruit was described for the first time by John Lindley.

December 2003 & January 2004

29 MONDAY

30 TUESDAY *First Quarter*

31 WEDNESDAY *New Year's Eve*

1 THURSDAY *New Year's Day*
Holiday UK, Republic of Ireland,
Canada, USA, Australia and New Zealand

2 FRIDAY *Holiday, Scotland and New Zealand*

3 SATURDAY

4 SUNDAY

Cattleya loddigesii, a hand-coloured engraving after a drawing by John Lindley, from his *Collectanea botanica* (1821). Both the genus and the species were named by Lindley.

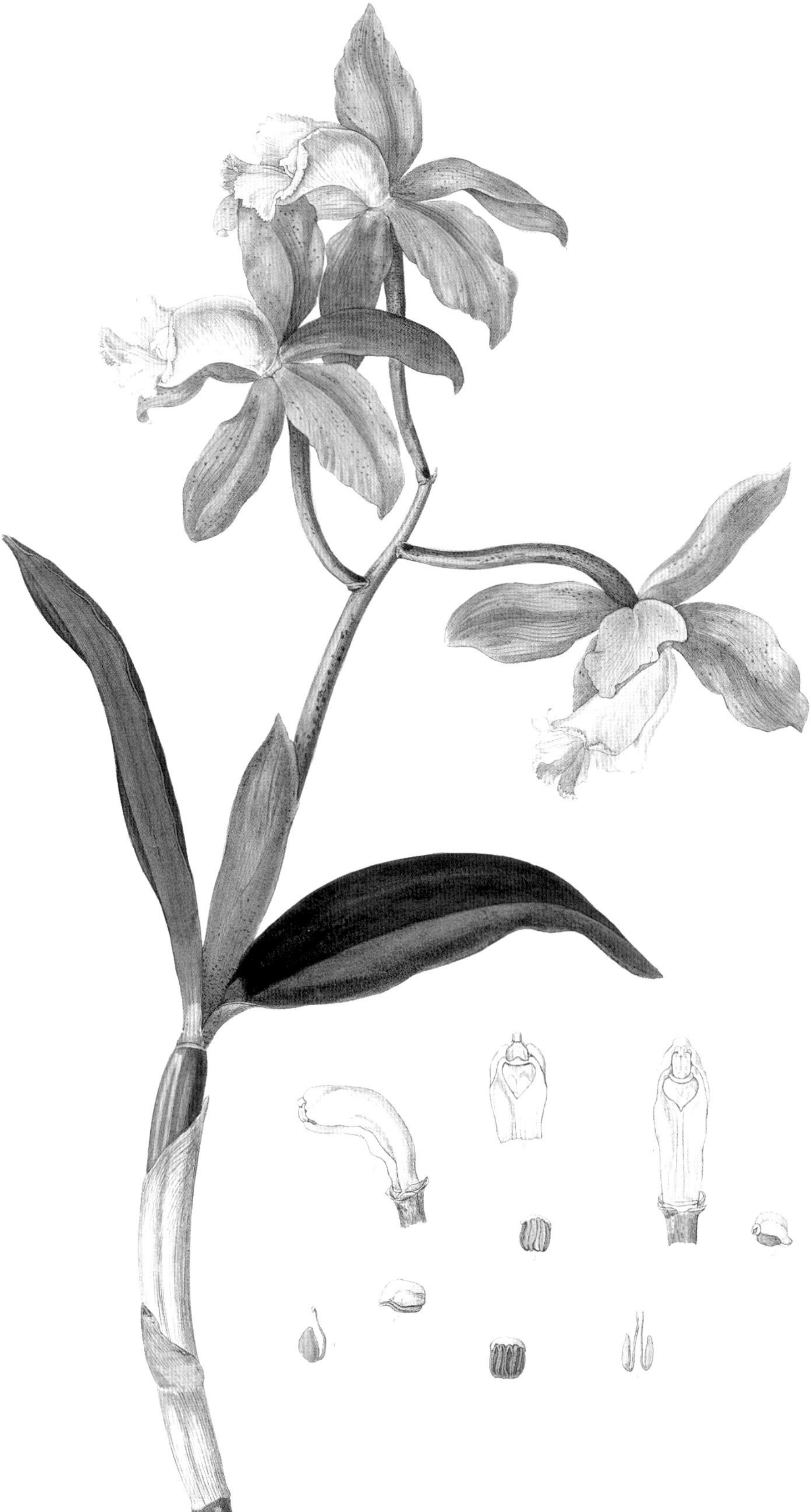

5 MONDAY

6 TUESDAY Epiphany

7 WEDNESDAY *Full Moon*

8 THURSDAY

9 FRIDAY

10 SATURDAY

11 SUNDAY

Crocus pusillus (now *C. biflorus*), a hand-coloured engraving after a drawing by Miss S. A. Drake (*fl.* 1820s–1840s), from the 23rd volume of the *Botanical Register* (1837), edited by John Lindley

January WEEK 3

12 MONDAY

13 TUESDAY

14 WEDNESDAY

15 THURSDAY *Last Quarter*

16 FRIDAY

17 SATURDAY

18 SUNDAY

Berberis nepalensis (now *vulgaris*), a hand-retouched chromolithograph by Louis-Aristide-Léon Constans (*fl.* 1830s–1860s), from the third volume of *Paxton's Flower Garden* (1852–1853) by John Lindley and Joseph Paxton

19 MONDAY *Holiday, USA (Martin Luther King's birthday)*

20 TUESDAY *RHS London Flower Show*

21 WEDNESDAY *New Moon* *RHS London Flower Show*

22 THURSDAY *Chinese New Year*

23 FRIDAY

24 SATURDAY

25 SUNDAY

Helleborus atrorubens, a hand-retouched chromolithograph by Louis-Aristide-Léon Constans (*fl.* 1830s–1860s), from the third volume of *Paxton's Flower Garden* (1852–1853) by John Lindley and Joseph Paxton

January & February

WEEK 5

26 MONDAY *Holiday, Australia (Australia Day)*

27 TUESDAY

28 WEDNESDAY

29 THURSDAY *First Quarter*

30 FRIDAY

31 SATURDAY

1 SUNDAY

Garrya elliptica, a hand-coloured engraving after a drawing by Miss S. A. Drake (*fl.* 1820s–1840s), from the 20th volume of the *Botanical Register* (1834–1835), edited by John Lindley. This plant was discovered by the Horticultural Society's collector David Douglas and first described by Lindley.

February

2 MONDAY

3 TUESDAY

4 WEDNESDAY

5 THURSDAY

6 FRIDAY *Full Moon* *Holiday, New Zealand (Waitangi Day)*

7 SATURDAY

8 SUNDAY

Disa grandiflora, a hand-coloured engraving after a drawing by Miss S. A. Drake (*fl.* 1820s–1840s), from John Lindley's *Sertum orchidaceum* (1838–1841)

February WEEK 7

9 MONDAY

10 TUESDAY

11 WEDNESDAY

12 THURSDAY *Holiday, USA (Lincoln's birthday)*

13 FRIDAY *Last Quarter*

14 SATURDAY *St Valentine's Day*

15 SUNDAY

Now known as *Sequoiadendron giganteum*, this tree was named *Wellingtonia gigantea* by John Lindley in 1853. The chromolithograph was published in 1884 in the *Pinetum Britannicum*, edited by E. J. Ravenscroft; Lindley had been a collaborator when the work was begun in 1863.

16 MONDAY *Holiday, USA (Presidents' Day)*

17 TUESDAY *RHS London Flower Show*

18 WEDNESDAY *RHS London Flower Show*

19 THURSDAY

20 FRIDAY *New Moon*

21 SATURDAY

22 SUNDAY *Islamic New Year (subject to sighting of the moon)*

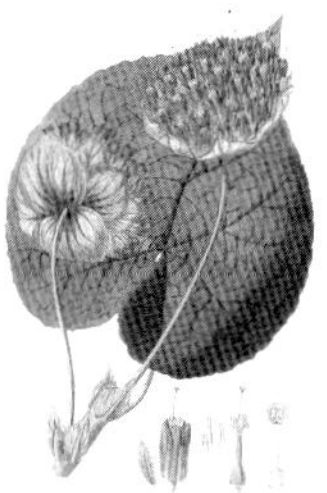

Astrapaea wallichii, a hand-coloured engraving after a drawing by John Lindley from his *Collectanea botanica* (1821)

February
WEEK 9

23 MONDAY

24 TUESDAY *Shrove Tuesday*

25 WEDNESDAY *Ash Wednesday*

26 THURSDAY

27 FRIDAY

28 SATURDAY *First Quarter*

29 SUNDAY

Catasetum atratum, a hand-coloured engraving after a drawing by Miss S. A. Drake (*fl.* 1820s–1840s), from the 24th volume of the *Botanical Register* (1838), edited by John Lindley. This plant was named by Lindley.

1 MONDAY St David's Day

2 TUESDAY

3 WEDNESDAY

4 THURSDAY

5 FRIDAY

6 SATURDAY *Full Moon*

7 SUNDAY

Forsythia viridissima, an unsigned chromolithograph from the second volume of *Jardin Fleuriste* (1851–1852) by Charles Lemaire, whose principal artist was Jean-Christophe Heyland (1792–1866). This plant was named and described by John Lindley in 1847.

March WEEK 11

8 MONDAY *Commonwealth Day*

9 TUESDAY *RHS London Flower Show*

10 WEDNESDAY *RHS London Flower Show*

11 THURSDAY

12 FRIDAY

13 SATURDAY *Last Quarter* *RHS London Orchid Show*

14 SUNDAY *RHS London Orchid Show*

Cypripedium (now *Paphiopedilum*) *purpuratum*, a hand-coloured engraving after a drawing by Miss S. A. Drake (*fl.* 1820s–1840s), from the 23rd volume of the *Botanical Register* (1837), edited by John Lindley

15 MONDAY

16 TUESDAY

17 WEDNESDAY

St Patrick's Day
Holiday, Northern Ireland and Republic of Ireland

18 THURSDAY

19 FRIDAY

20 SATURDAY *New Moon* *Vernal Equinox*

21 SUNDAY *Mothering Sunday, UK*

Erythronium grandiflorum, a hand-coloured engraving after a drawing by Miss S. A. Drake (*fl.* 1820s–1840s), from the 21st volume of the *Botanical Register* (1836), edited by John Lindley. This plant was discovered by the Horticultural Society's collector David Douglas and named by Lindley.

March WEEK 13

22 MONDAY

23 TUESDAY

24 WEDNESDAY

25 THURSDAY

26 FRIDAY

27 SATURDAY

28 SUNDAY *First Quarter* *British Summer Time begins*

Brownea ariza, the Ariza plant, a hand-retouched chromolithograph by Louis-Aristide-Léon Constans (*fl.* 1830s–1860s), from the second volume of *Paxton's Flower Garden* (1851–1852) by John Lindley and Joseph Paxton. The plant was collected by Theodor Hartweg for the Horticultural Society.

March & April

29 MONDAY

30 TUESDAY

31 WEDNESDAY

1 THURSDAY

2 FRIDAY

3 SATURDAY

4 SUNDAY *Palm Sunday*

Amaryllis solandraeflora (now *Hippeastrum solandraeflorum*), a hand-coloured engraving from John Lindley's *Collectanea botanica* (1821), of a plant both named and drawn by Lindley (from William Cattley's specimen)

April WEEK 15

5 MONDAY *Full Moon*

6 TUESDAY *Passover (Pesach), First Day*
RHS London Flower Show

7 WEDNESDAY *RHS London Flower Show*

8 THURSDAY *Maundy Thursday*

9 FRIDAY *Good Friday*
Holiday, UK, Republic of Ireland, Canada, USA, Australia and New Zealand

10 SATURDAY

11 SUNDAY *Easter Sunday*

Camellia reticulata, a hand-coloured engraving after a drawing by Alfred Chandler (1804–1896), from *Illustrations and Descriptions of the Plants which Compose the Natural Order Camellieae* (1831) by Chandler and William Beattie Booth. This plant was introduced into England by the Horticultural Society's collector John Damper Parks in 1824 and was named by John Lindley.

12 MONDAY *Last Quarter*

Easter Monday
Holiday, UK (exc. Scotland), Republic of Ireland, Canada, USA, Australia and New Zealand
Passover (Pesach), Seventh Day

13 TUESDAY

Passover (Pesach), Eighth Day

14 WEDNESDAY

15 THURSDAY

16 FRIDAY

17 SATURDAY

RHS Plant Road Show, Torquay (to be confirmed)

18 SUNDAY

RHS Plant Road Show, Torquay (to be confirmed)

Primula sinensis, a hand-coloured engraving from John Lindley's *Collectanea botanica* (1821) of a plant both named and drawn by Lindley

April WEEK 17

19 MONDAY *New Moon*

20 TUESDAY

21 WEDNESDAY *Birthday of Queen Elizabeth II*

22 THURSDAY

23 FRIDAY *St George's Day*

24 SATURDAY

25 SUNDAY

Varieties of *Tulipa scabriscapa*, a hand-coloured engraving after a drawing by Miss S. A. Drake (*fl.* 1820s–1840s), from the 23rd volume of the *Botanical Register* (1837), edited by John Lindley

WEEK 18 # *April & May*

26 MONDAY *Holiday, Australia and New Zealand (Anzac Day)*

27 TUESDAY *First Quarter* *RHS London Flower Show (to be confirmed)*

28 WEDNESDAY *RHS London Flower Show (to be confirmed)*

29 THURSDAY

30 FRIDAY

1 SATURDAY

2 SUNDAY

Myosotis azorica, the Azorean Forget-me-not, a hand-retouched chromolithograph by Louis-Aristide-Léon Constans (*fl.* 1830s–1860s), from the third volume of *Paxton's Flower Garden* (1852–1853) by John Lindley and Joseph Paxton

May WEEK 19

3 MONDAY *Early May Bank Holiday, UK and Republic of Ireland*

4 TUESDAY *Full Moon*

5 WEDNESDAY

6 THURSDAY

7 FRIDAY *Malvern Spring Gardening Show*

8 SATURDAY *Malvern Spring Gardening Show*

9 SUNDAY *Mother's Day, Canada, USA, Australia and New Zealand*
Malvern Spring Gardening Show

Rosa macrophylla, a hand-coloured engraving after a drawing by John Lindley from his *Rosarum monographia* (1820)

10 MONDAY

11 TUESDAY *Last Quarter*

12 WEDNESDAY

13 THURSDAY

14 FRIDAY

15 SATURDAY

16 SUNDAY

Now known as *Kennedia prostrata*, this plant was named *K. maryattae* by John Lindley. The hand-coloured engraving, after a drawing by Miss S. A. Drake (*fl.* 1820s–1840s), was published in the 21st volume of the *Botanical Register* (1836), edited by Lindley.

May WEEK 21

17 MONDAY

18 TUESDAY

19 WEDNESDAY *New Moon*

20 THURSDAY *Ascension Day*

21 FRIDAY

22 SATURDAY

23 SUNDAY

The 'Turkey' apricot, a hand-coloured engraving after a drawing by Augusta Innes Withers (1792–1869), from the first volume of John Lindley's *Pomological Magazine* (1827–1828)

24 MONDAY *Holiday, Canada (Victoria Day)*

25 TUESDAY *Chelsea Flower Show*

26 WEDNESDAY *Jewish Festival of Weeks (Shavuot)*
Chelsea Flower Show

27 THURSDAY *First Quarter* *Chelsea Flower Show*

28 FRIDAY *Chelsea Flower Show*

29 SATURDAY

30 SUNDAY *Whit Sunday (Pentecost)*

The graft-hybrid + *Laburnocytisus* 'Adami', a hand-coloured engraving after a drawing by Miss S. A. Drake (*fl.* 1820s–1840s), from the 23rd volume of the *Botanical Register* (1837), edited by John Lindley

May & June WEEK 23

31 MONDAY *Spring Bank Holiday, UK*
Holiday, USA (Memorial Day)

1 TUESDAY

2 WEDNESDAY

3 THURSDAY *Full Moon*

4 FRIDAY

5 SATURDAY

6 SUNDAY *Trinity Sunday*

Odontoglossum laeve, a chromolithograph after a drawing by Walter Hood Fitch (1817–1892) of an orchid named by John Lindley and published in James Bateman's *Monograph of Odontoglossum* (1874)

7 MONDAY *Holiday, New Zealand (The Queen's birthday)*

8 TUESDAY

9 WEDNESDAY *Last Quarter*

10 THURSDAY *Corpus Christi*

11 FRIDAY

12 SATURDAY *The Queen's official birthday (subject to confirmation)*

13 SUNDAY

The 'deep blood-coloured moutan' (a variety of *Paeonia suffruticosa*), a hand-retouched chromolithograph by Louis-Aristide-Léon Constans (*fl.* 1830s–1860s), from the first volume of *Paxton's Flower Garden* (1850–1851) by John Lindley and Joseph Paxton

June WEEK 25

14 MONDAY *Holiday, Australia (The Queen's Birthday)*

15 TUESDAY

16 WEDNESDAY *BBC Gardeners' World Live, Birmingham*

17 THURSDAY *New Moon* *BBC Gardeners' World Live, Birmingham*

18 FRIDAY *BBC Gardeners' World Live, Birmingham*

19 SATURDAY *BBC Gardeners' World Live, Birmingham*

20 SUNDAY *Father's Day, UK, Canada and USA*
BBC Gardeners' World Live, Birmingham

Gooseberry 'Crompton's Sheba Queen', a hand-coloured engraving after a drawing by Augusta Innes Withers (1792–1869), from the first volume of John Lindley's *Pomological Magazine* (1827–1828)

21 MONDAY *Summer Solstice*

22 TUESDAY *First Wisley Flower Show*

23 WEDNESDAY *First Wisley Flower Show*

24 THURSDAY *First Wisley Flower Show*

25 FRIDAY *First Quarter*

26 SATURDAY

27 SUNDAY

Papaver bracteatum, a hand-coloured engraving from John Lindley's *Collectanea botanica* (1821), of a plant both named and drawn by Lindley

June & July WEEK 27

28 MONDAY

29 TUESDAY

30 WEDNESDAY

1 THURSDAY *Holiday, Canada (Canada Day)*
RHS London Flower Show

2 FRIDAY *Full Moon* *RHS London Flower Show*

3 SATURDAY *RHS London Flower Show*

4 SUNDAY *Independence Day, USA*

Allium caeruleum, a hand-coloured engraving after a drawing by Miss S. A. Drake (*fl.* 1820s–1840s), from the 26th volume of the *Botanical Register* (1840), edited by John Lindley

2
3
1

5 MONDAY *Holiday, USA (Independence Day)*

6 TUESDAY *Hampton Court Palace Flower Show*

7 WEDNESDAY *Hampton Court Palace Flower Show*

8 THURSDAY *Hampton Court Palace Flower Show*

9 FRIDAY *Last Quarter* *Hampton Court Palace Flower Show*

10 SATURDAY *Hampton Court Palace Flower Show*

11 SUNDAY *Hampton Court Palace Flower Show*

Mandevilla suaveolens, a hand-coloured engraving after a drawing by Miss S. A. Drake (*fl.* 1820s–1840s), from the 26th volume of the *Botanical Register* (1840), edited by John Lindley. This plant was named by Lindley.

July

WEEK 29

12 MONDAY *Holiday, Northern Ireland (Battle of the Boyne)*

13 TUESDAY

14 WEDNESDAY

15 THURSDAY *St Swithin's Day*

16 FRIDAY

17 SATURDAY *New Moon*

18 SUNDAY

The 'Barnet' raspberry, a hand-coloured engraving after a drawing by Augusta Innes Withers (1792–1869), from the first volume of John Lindley's *Pomological Magazine* (1827–1828)

19 MONDAY

20 TUESDAY

21 WEDNESDAY *The RHS Flower Show at Tatton Park*

22 THURSDAY *The RHS Flower Show at Tatton Park*

23 FRIDAY *The RHS Flower Show at Tatton Park*

24 SATURDAY *The RHS Flower Show at Tatton Park*

25 SUNDAY *First Quarter* *The RHS Flower Show at Tatton Park*

Iris alata (now *planifolia*), a hand-coloured engraving after a drawing by Miss S. A. Drake (*fl.* 1820s–1840s), from the 22nd volume of the *Botanical Register* (1836), edited by John Lindley

July & August WEEK 31

26 MONDAY

27 TUESDAY

28 WEDNESDAY

29 THURSDAY

30 FRIDAY

31 SATURDAY *Full Moon*

1 SUNDAY

Rosa woodsii, an original drawing in watercolour by John Lindley, dated 1821. Lindley named this species in 1820 from a specimen from the Missouri River area.

2 MONDAY *Summer Bank Holiday, Scotland and Republic of Ireland*

3 TUESDAY

4 WEDNESDAY

5 THURSDAY

6 FRIDAY

7 SATURDAY *Last Quarter*

8 SUNDAY

Clematis lanuginosa, a hand-retouched chromolithograph by Louis-Aristide-Léon Constans (*fl.* 1830s–1860s), from the third volume of *Paxton's Flower Garden* (1852–1853) by John Lindley and Joseph Paxton. This species had first flowered in cultivation that year, in the nursery of Standish and Noble.

August WEEK 33

9 MONDAY

10 TUESDAY

11 WEDNESDAY

12 THURSDAY

13 FRIDAY

14 SATURDAY

15 SUNDAY

Rosa sulphurea (now *R. hemisphaerica*), a hand-coloured engraving after a drawing by John Curtis (1791–1862), from John Lindley's *Rosarum monographia* (1820)

16 MONDAY *New Moon*

17 TUESDAY *Second Wisley Flower Show*

18 WEDNESDAY *Second Wisley Flower Show*

19 THURSDAY *Second Wisley Flower Show*

20 FRIDAY

21 SATURDAY

22 SUNDAY

Tacsonia (now *Passiflora*) *manicata*, a hand-retouched chromolithograph by Louis-Aristide-Léon Constans (*fl.* 1830s–1860s), from the first volume of *Paxton's Flower Garden* (1850–1851) by John Lindley and Joseph Paxton

August WEEK 35

23 MONDAY *First Quarter*

24 TUESDAY

25 WEDNESDAY

26 THURSDAY

27 FRIDAY

28 SATURDAY

29 SUNDAY

Digitalis ambigua (now *grandiflora*), a hand-coloured engraving after a drawing by Ferdinand Bauer (1760–1826), from John Lindley's *Digitalium monographia* (1821)

WEEK 36 # *August & September*

30 MONDAY *Full Moon* *Summer Bank Holiday, UK (exc. Scotland)*

31 TUESDAY

1 WEDNESDAY

2 THURSDAY

3 FRIDAY

4 SATURDAY

5 SUNDAY *Father's Day, Australia and New Zealand*

Clematis florida 'Bicolor', a hand-coloured engraving after a drawing by Miss S. A. Drake (fl. 1820s–1840s), from the 24th volume of the *Botanical Register* (1838), edited by John Lindley

September WEEK 37

6 MONDAY *Last Quarter* *Holiday, Canada (Labour Day) and USA (Labor Day)*

7 TUESDAY

8 WEDNESDAY

9 THURSDAY

10 FRIDAY

11 SATURDAY

12 SUNDAY

Anemone japonica, a hand-coloured engraving after a drawing by Miss S. A. Drake (*fl.* 1820s–1840s), from the 31st volume of the *Botanical Register* (1845), edited by John Lindley. Although described in the 18th century, it was not grown in England until Robert Fortune introduced it through the Horticultural Society in 1844.

September

13 MONDAY

14 TUESDAY *New Moon* *RHS Great Autumn Show, London*

15 WEDNESDAY *RHS Great Autumn Show, London*

16 THURSDAY *Jewish New Year (Rosh Hashanah)*

17 FRIDAY

18 SATURDAY

19 SUNDAY

Canna speciosa (now *C. coccinea*), a hand-coloured engraving by M. Hart, from the 15th volume of the *Botanical Register* (1829), the first volume to be edited by John Lindley

September WEEK 39

20 MONDAY

21 TUESDAY *First Quarter*

22 WEDNESDAY *Autumnal Equinox*

23 THURSDAY

24 FRIDAY

25 SATURDAY *Jewish Day of Atonement (Yom Kippur)*
Malvern Autumn Garden and Country Show

26 SUNDAY *Malvern Autumn Garden and Country Show*

Passiflora × caeruleoracemosa (now *P. × violacea*), the first hybrid passion flower; a hand-coloured engraving after a drawing by John Lindley, from the *Transactions of the Horticultural Society* (1820)

September & October

27 MONDAY

28 TUESDAY *Full Moon*

29 WEDNESDAY *Michaelmas Day*

30 THURSDAY *Jewish Festival of Tabernacles (Succoth), First Day*

1 FRIDAY

2 SATURDAY

3 SUNDAY

Sollya linearis, a hand-coloured engraving after a drawing by Miss S. A. Drake (*fl.* 1820s–1840s), from the 26th volume of the *Botanical Register* (1840), edited by John Lindley, who also named the plant

October

WEEK 41

4 MONDAY

5 TUESDAY *RHS London Flower Show*

6 WEDNESDAY *Last Quarter* *RHS London Flower Show*

7 THURSDAY *Jewish Festival of Tabernacles (Succoth), Eighth Day*

8 FRIDAY

9 SATURDAY

10 SUNDAY

Laelia superbiens, a species named by John Lindley but now included in the genus *Schomburgkia*. This hand-retouched chromolithograph after a drawing by Miss S. A. Drake (*fl.* 1820s–1840s), is from *The Orchidaceae of Mexico and Guatemala* (1843) by James Bateman (1811–1897).

11 MONDAY *Holiday, Canada (Thanksgiving Day)*
Holiday, USA (Columbus Day)

12 TUESDAY

13 WEDNESDAY

14 THURSDAY *New Moon*

15 FRIDAY *First Day of Ramadan (subject to sighting of the moon)*

16 SATURDAY

17 SUNDAY

Oxyramphis (now *Lespedeza*) *macrostyla*, a hand-coloured engraving after a drawing by Miss S. A. Drake (*fl.* 1820s–1840s), from the 32nd volume of the *Botanical Register* (1846), edited by John Lindley. This plant was introduced into England through the Horticultural Society in 1845.

October

WEEK 43

18 MONDAY

19 TUESDAY

20 WEDNESDAY *First Quarter*

21 THURSDAY

22 FRIDAY

23 SATURDAY

24 SUNDAY *United Nations Day*

Hibiscus syriacus var. *chinensis*, a hand-retouched chromolithograph by Louis-Aristide-Léon Constans (*fl.* 1830s–1860s), from the third volume of *Paxton's Flower Garden* (1852–1853) by John Lindley and Joseph Paxton

WEEK 44 # October

25 MONDAY

Holiday, Republic of Ireland
Holiday, New Zealand (Labour Day)

26 TUESDAY

27 WEDNESDAY

28 THURSDAY *Full Moon*

29 FRIDAY

30 SATURDAY

31 SUNDAY

Hallowe'en
British Summer Time ends

Mimulus cardinalis, a hand-coloured engraving, after a drawing by Miss S. A. Drake (*fl.* 1820s–1840s), from the *Transactions of the Horticultural Society* (1835). The plant was discovered and named by the Horticultural Society's collector David Douglas, and John Lindley published the first description.

November

WEEK 45

1 MONDAY All Saints' Day

2 TUESDAY

3 WEDNESDAY

4 THURSDAY

5 FRIDAY *Last Quarter* Guy Fawkes' Day

6 SATURDAY

7 SUNDAY

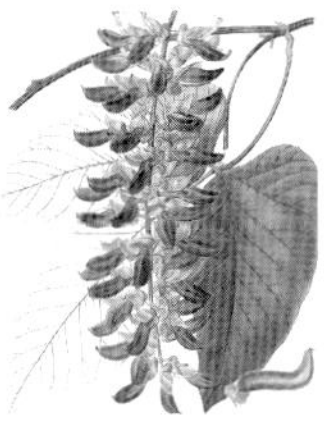

Mucuna pruriens, a hand-coloured engraving after a drawing by Miss S. A. Drake (*fl.* 1820s–1840s), from the 24th volume of the *Botanical Register* (1838), edited by John Lindley

WEEK 46 # November

8 MONDAY

9 TUESDAY

10 WEDNESDAY

11 THURSDAY *Holiday, Canada (Remembrance Day)*
Holiday, USA (Veterans' Day)

12 FRIDAY *New Moon*

13 SATURDAY

14 SUNDAY *Remembrance Sunday, UK*

Portulaca thellusonii, a hand-coloured engraving after a drawing by Miss S. A. Drake (*fl.* 1820s–1840s), from the 26th volume of the *Botanical Register* (1840), edited by John Lindley. This plant was named by Lindley.

November WEEK 47

15 MONDAY

16 TUESDAY

17 WEDNESDAY

18 THURSDAY

19 FRIDAY *First Quarter*

20 SATURDAY

21 SUNDAY

The 'Common Muscadine' grape, a hand-coloured engraving after a drawing by Augusta Innes Withers (1792–1869), from the first volume of John Lindley's *Pomological Magazine* (1827–1828)

22 MONDAY

23 TUESDAY *RHS London Flower Show*

24 WEDNESDAY *RHS London Flower Show*

25 THURSDAY *Holiday, USA (Thanksgiving Day)*

26 FRIDAY *Full Moon*

27 SATURDAY

28 SUNDAY *Advent Sunday*

Grammatophyllum speciosum, a hand-retouched chromolithograph by Louis-Aristide-Léon Constans (*fl.* 1830s–1860s), from the second volume of *Paxton's Flower Garden* (1851–1852) by John Lindley and Joseph Paxton

November & December WEEK 49

29 MONDAY

30 TUESDAY *St Andrew's Day*

1 WEDNESDAY

2 THURSDAY

3 FRIDAY

4 SATURDAY

5 SUNDAY *Last Quarter*

Now known as *Encyclia vitellina*, this orchid was named *Epidendrum vitellinum* by John Lindley. The hand-coloured engraving after a drawing by Miss S. A. Drake (*fl.* 1820s–40s), is from Lindley's *Sertum orchidaceum* (1838–1841).

6 MONDAY

7 TUESDAY

8 WEDNESDAY *Jewish Festival of Chanukah, First Day*

9 THURSDAY

10 FRIDAY

11 SATURDAY

12 SUNDAY *New Moon*

Dendrobium caerulescens (now *D. nobile*), a hand-coloured engraving after a drawing by Miss S. A. Drake (*fl.* 1820s–1840s), from John Lindley's *Sertum orchidaceum* (1838–1841)

December

WEEK 51

13 MONDAY

14 TUESDAY

15 WEDNESDAY

16 THURSDAY

17 FRIDAY

18 SATURDAY *First Quarter*

19 SUNDAY

Now know as *Bromelia antiacantha*, this plant was named *B. fastuosa* by John Lindley. The hand-coloured engraving after a drawing by Lindley is from his *Collectanea botanica* (1821).

WEEK 52 **December**

20 MONDAY

21 TUESDAY *Winter Solstice*

22 WEDNESDAY

23 THURSDAY

24 FRIDAY *Christmas Eve*
Holiday, USA (Christmas Day observed)

25 SATURDAY *Christmas Day*

26 SUNDAY *Full Moon* *Boxing Day (St Stephen's Day)*

Amaryllis vittata major, now classified as a form of *Hippeastrum vittatum*, a hand-coloured engraving after a drawing by John Lindley from his *Collectanea botanica* (1821)

December 2004 & January 2005

WEEK 53

27 MONDAY

Holiday, UK, Republic of Ireland, Canada, Australia and New Zealand

28 TUESDAY

Holiday, UK, Republic of Ireland, Canada, Australia and New Zealand

29 WEDNESDAY

30 THURSDAY

31 FRIDAY

New Year's Eve
Holiday, USA: New Year's Day observed

1 SATURDAY

New Year's Day

2 SUNDAY

Cattleya labiata, a hand-coloured engraving after a drawing by John Lindley from his *Collectanea botanica* (1821). Lindley named the genus, of which this is the type specimen, in honour of his patron William Cattley.

CALENDAR 2004

JANUARY

M	T	W	T	F	S	S
			1	2	3	4
5	6	7	8	9	10	11
12	13	14	15	16	17	18
19	20	21	22	23	24	25
26	27	28	29	30	31	

FEBRUARY

M	T	W	T	F	S	S
						1
2	3	4	5	6	7	8
9	10	11	12	13	14	15
16	17	18	19	20	21	22
23	24	25	26	27	28	29

MARCH

M	T	W	T	F	S	S
1	2	3	4	5	6	7
8	9	10	11	12	13	14
15	16	17	18	19	20	21
22	23	24	25	26	27	28
29	30	31				

APRIL

M	T	W	T	F	S	S
			1	2	3	4
5	6	7	8	9	10	11
12	13	14	15	16	17	18
19	20	21	22	23	24	25
26	27	28	29	30		

MAY

M	T	W	T	F	S	S
					1	2
3	4	5	6	7	8	9
10	11	12	13	14	15	16
17	18	19	20	21	22	23
24	25	26	27	28	29	30
31						

JUNE

M	T	W	T	F	S	S
	1	2	3	4	5	6
7	8	9	10	11	12	13
14	15	16	17	18	19	20
21	22	23	24	25	26	27
28	29	30				

JULY

M	T	W	T	F	S	S
			1	2	3	4
5	6	7	8	9	10	11
12	13	14	15	16	17	18
19	20	21	22	23	24	25
26	27	28	29	30	31	

AUGUST

M	T	W	T	F	S	S
						1
2	3	4	5	6	7	8
9	10	11	12	13	14	15
16	17	18	19	20	21	22
23	24	25	26	27	28	29
30	31					

SEPTEMBER

M	T	W	T	F	S	S
		1	2	3	4	5
6	7	8	9	10	11	12
13	14	15	16	17	18	19
20	21	22	23	24	25	26
27	28	29	30			

OCTOBER

M	T	W	T	F	S	S
				1	2	3
4	5	6	7	8	9	10
11	12	13	14	15	16	17
18	19	20	21	22	23	24
25	26	27	28	29	30	31

NOVEMBER

M	T	W	T	F	S	S
1	2	3	4	5	6	7
8	9	10	11	12	13	14
15	16	17	18	19	20	21
22	23	24	25	26	27	28
29	30					

DECEMBER

M	T	W	T	F	S	S
		1	2	3	4	5
6	7	8	9	10	11	12
13	14	15	16	17	18	19
20	21	22	23	24	25	26
27	28	29	30	31		

CALENDAR 2005

JANUARY

M	T	W	T	F	S	S
					1	2
3	4	5	6	7	8	9
10	11	12	13	14	15	16
17	18	19	20	21	22	23
24	25	26	27	28	29	30
31						

FEBRUARY

M	T	W	T	F	S	S
	1	2	3	4	5	6
7	8	9	10	11	12	13
14	15	16	17	18	19	20
21	22	23	24	25	26	27
28						

MARCH

M	T	W	T	F	S	S
	1	2	3	4	5	6
7	8	9	10	11	12	13
14	15	16	17	18	19	20
21	22	23	24	25	26	27
28	29	30	31			

APRIL

M	T	W	T	F	S	S
				1	2	3
4	5	6	7	8	9	10
11	12	13	14	15	16	17
18	19	20	21	22	23	24
25	26	27	28	29	30	

MAY

M	T	W	T	F	S	S
						1
2	3	4	5	6	7	8
9	10	11	12	13	14	15
16	17	18	19	20	21	22
23	24	25	26	27	28	29
30	31					

JUNE

M	T	W	T	F	S	S
		1	2	3	4	5
6	7	8	9	10	11	12
13	14	15	16	17	18	19
20	21	22	23	24	25	26
27	28	29	30			

JULY

M	T	W	T	F	S	S
				1	2	3
4	5	6	7	8	9	10
11	12	13	14	15	16	17
18	19	20	21	22	23	24
25	26	27	28	29	30	31

AUGUST

M	T	W	T	F	S	S
1	2	3	4	5	6	7
8	9	10	11	12	13	14
15	16	17	18	19	20	21
22	23	24	25	26	27	28
29	30	31				

SEPTEMBER

M	T	W	T	F	S	S
			1	2	3	4
5	6	7	8	9	10	11
12	13	14	15	16	17	18
19	20	21	22	23	24	25
26	27	28	29	30		

OCTOBER

M	T	W	T	F	S	S
					1	2
3	4	5	6	7	8	9
10	11	12	13	14	15	16
17	18	19	20	21	22	23
24	25	26	27	28	29	30
31						

NOVEMBER

M	T	W	T	F	S	S
	1	2	3	4	5	6
7	8	9	10	11	12	13
14	15	16	17	18	19	20
21	22	23	24	25	26	27
28	29	30				

DECEMBER

M	T	W	T	F	S	S
			1	2	3	4
5	6	7	8	9	10	11
12	13	14	15	16	17	18
19	20	21	22	23	24	25
26	27	28	29	30	31	